This
Treasure Cove Story
belongs to

ANT-MAN

A CENTUM BOOK 978-1-912396-76-4
Published in Great Britain by Centum Books Ltd.
This edition published 2018.

1 3 5 7 9 10 8 6 4 2

Centum Books Ltd, 20 Devon Square, Newton Abbot,
Devon, TQ12 2HR, UK.

www.centumbooksltd.co.uk | books@centumbooksltd.co.uk
CENTUM BOOKS Limited Reg. No. 07641486.

A CIP catalogue record for this book is available
from the British Library.

Printed in China.

centum

MARVEL
ANT-MAN

By Billy Wrecks
Illustrated by Patrick Spaziante

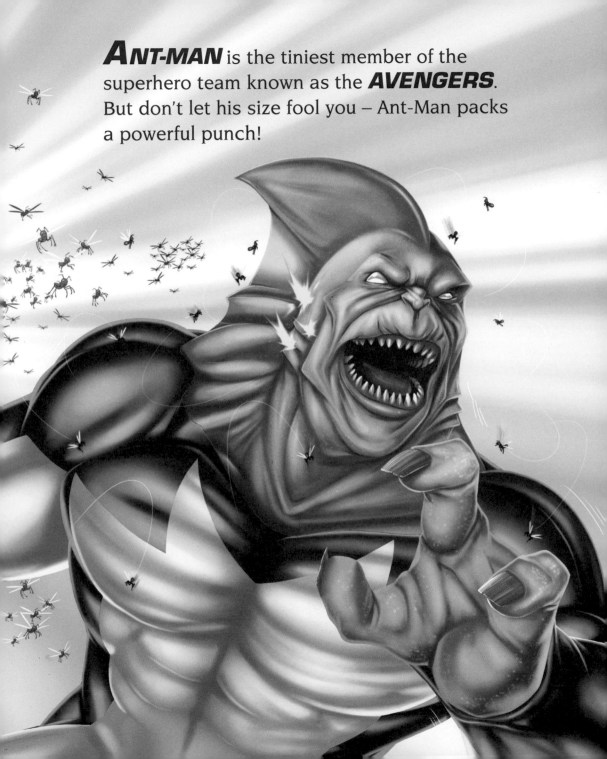

ANT-MAN is the tiniest member of the superhero team known as the **AVENGERS**. But don't let his size fool you – Ant-Man packs a powerful punch!

Ant-Man's real name is Scott Lang.
He was once a thief, but he had a good heart.
A scientist named Dr Hank Pym saw the
potential in the young man. He gave Lang
the chance to become a hero.

Whenever he is exposed to Dr Pym's amazing Pym Particles, Scott Lang shrinks to only half an inch tall!

Using the special helmet, wrist blasters and super-suit created by Dr Pym, Lang goes into action as the **ASTONISHING ANT-MAN**. There's no secret lair this tiny hero can't sneak into.

Even when he is small, Ant-Man has the strength of a full-grown man.
That can be quite a surprise for the bad guys!

'Feel my sting!' Ant-Man shouts. He uses his wrist blasters to deliver powerful shocks.

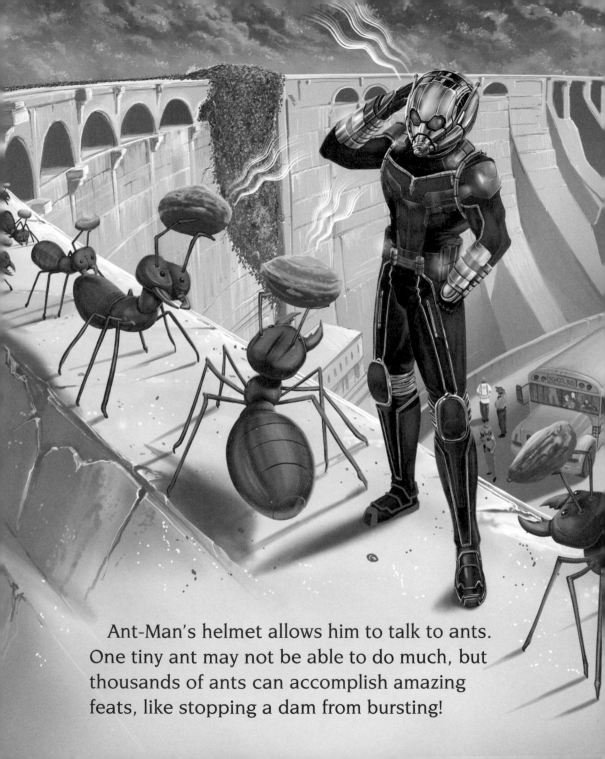

Ant-Man's helmet allows him to talk to ants. One tiny ant may not be able to do much, but thousands of ants can accomplish amazing feats, like stopping a dam from bursting!

As a member of the Avengers, Ant-Man fights all kinds of evildoers alongside such heroes as the Hulk, Hawkeye, Black Widow, Thor, Iron Man and Captain America.

'Bring on the bad guys!' Ant-Man
shouts as he flies into action.

ULTRON is an almost indestructible robot created by Dr Pym to help mankind. The robot went bad and now it wants to destroy the world.

'Download this!' Ant-Man says, putting a stop to Ultron's copies of himself.

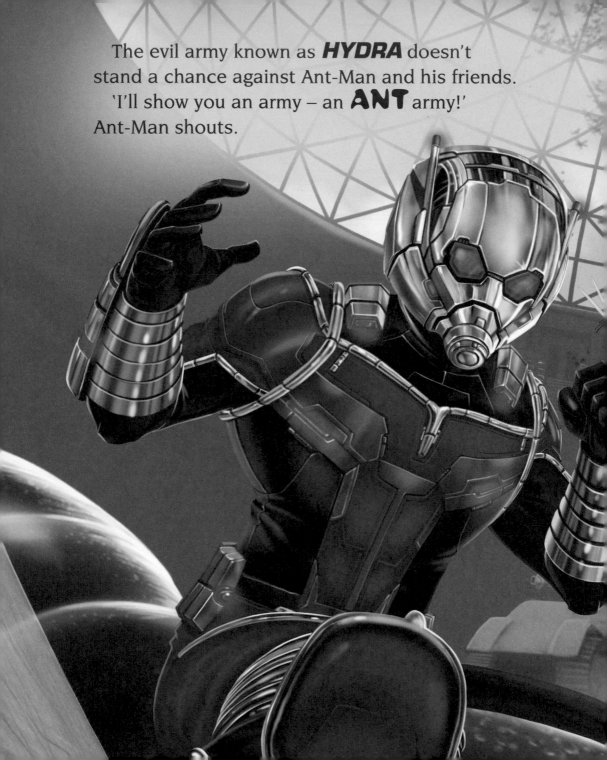

The evil army known as **HYDRA** doesn't stand a chance against Ant-Man and his friends. 'I'll show you an army – an **ANT** army!' Ant-Man shouts.

Sometimes it takes Ant-Man and all
the Avengers to fight one villain, such
as **COUNT NEFARIA**, who has
many superpowers…

...and sometimes they fight whole teams of super villains, such as the **MASTERS OF EVIL**, who combine their powers in hopes of defeating the heroes and taking over the world.

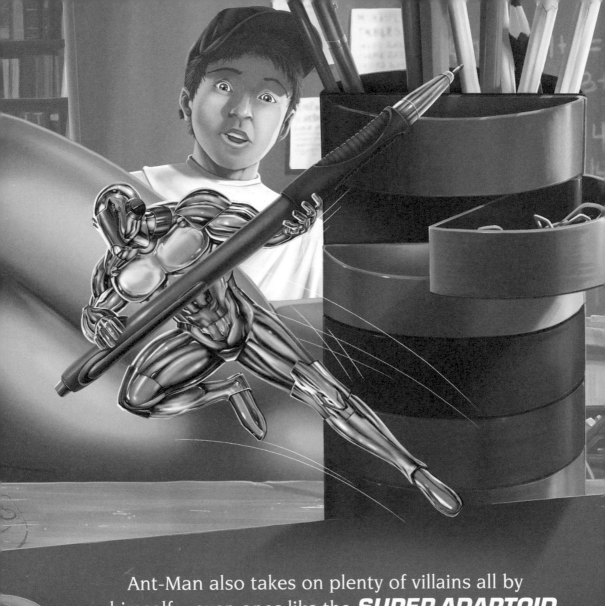

Ant-Man also takes on plenty of villains all by himself – even ones like the **SUPER ADAPTOID**, who can mimic any superhero's powers. The robot can shrink like Ant-Man!

'This desk isn't big enough for the both of us,' Ant-Man says.

Big or small, everyone looks up to the little
hero, Ant-Man!
GO, ANT-MAN!

Treasure Cove Stories

1 Three Little Pigs
2 Snow White and
The Seven Dwarfs
3 The Fox and the Hound
- Hide-and-Seek
4 Dumbo
5 Cinderella
6 Cinderella's Friends
7 Alice in Wonderland
8 Mad Hatter's Tea Party
from Alice in Wonderland
9 Mickey Mouse and
his Spaceship
10 Peter Pan
11 Pinocchio
12 The Prince and the Pauper
13 Sleeping Beauty
and the Good Fairies
14 The Lucky Puppy
15 Chicken Little
16 Santa's Toy Shop
17 Coco
18 Winnie-the-Pooh
and Tigger
19 The Sword in the Stone
20 Mary Poppins
21 The Jungle Book
22 The Aristocats
23 Lady and the Tramp
24 Bambi
25 Bambi - Friends of the Forest
26 Pete's Dragon
27 Beauty and the Beast
- The Teapot's Tale
28 Monsters, Inc.
- M is for Monster
29 Finding Nemo
30 The Incredibles
31 The Incredibles
- Jack-Jack Attack
32 Ratatouille
- Your Friend the Rat
33 Wall·E
34 Up
35 Princess and the Frog
36 Toy Story - The Pet Problem
37 Dora the Explorer
- Dora and the Unicorn King

38 Dora the Explorer
- Grandma's House
39 Spider-Man
- Night of the Vulture!
40 Wreck-it Ralph
41 Brave
42 The Invincible Iron Man
- Eye of the Dragon
43 SpongeBob SquarePants
- Sponge in Space!
44 SpongeBob SquarePants
- Where the Pirates Arrrgh!
45 Toy Story
- A Roaring Adventure
46 Cars - Deputy Mater
Saves the Day!
47 Spider-Man
- Trapped By The Green Goblin!
48 Big Hero 6
49 Spider-Man - High Voltage!
50 Frozen
51 Cinderella Is My Babysitter
52 Beauty and the Beast
- I Am The Beast
53 Blaze and the Monster
Machines - Mighty Monster
Machines
54 Blaze and the Monster
Machines - Dino Parade!
55 Teenage Mutant Ninja Turtles
- Follow The Ninja!
56 I Am A Princess
57 Paw Patrol
- The Big Book of Paw Patrol
58 Paw Patrol
- Adventures with Grandpa!
59 Merida Is Our Babysitter
60 Trolls
61 Trolls Holiday Special
62 The Secret Life of Pets
63 Zootropolis
64 Ariel Is My Babysitter
65 Inside Out
66 Belle Is My Babysitter
67 The Lion Guard
- Eye In The Sky
68 Moana
69 Finding Dory

70 Guardians of the Galaxy
71 Captain America
- High-Stakes Heist!
72 Ant-Man
73 The Mighty Avengers
74 The Mighty Avengers
- Lights Out!
75 The Incredible Hulk
76 Shimmer & Shine
- Wish upon a Sleepover
77 Shimmer & Shine
- Backyard Ballet
78 Paw Patrol - All-Star Pups!
79 Teenage Mutant Ninja Turtles
- Really Spaced Out!
80 Cars 2 - Travel Buddies
81 Madagascar
82 Jasmine Is My Babysitter
83 How To Train Your Dragon
84 Shrek
85 Puss In Boots
86 Kung Fu Panda
87 Beauty and the Beast
- I Am Belle
88 The Lion Guard
- The Imaginary Okapi
89 Thor - Thunder Strike!
90 Guardians of the Galaxy
-Rocket to the Rescue!
91 Nella The Princess Knight
- Nella and the Dragon
92 Shimmer & Shine
- Treasure Twins!
93 Olaf's Frozen Adventure
94 Black Panther
95 Branch's Bunker Birthday
96 Shimmer & Shine
- Pet Talent Show
97 The Ugly Duckling
98 Look Out for Mater!
99 101 Dalmatians
100 The Sorcerer's Apprentice
101 Tangled
102 Vampirina
- The Littlest Vampire
103 Puppy Dog Pals
- Don't Rain on my Pug-Rade

•Book list may be subject to change.